## BEETLE BAILEY: NEW OUTFIT!

Here's another in the happy series of books based on one of the most famous comic strips in the country. Once again the madcap inmates of Camp Swampy valiantly strive to overcome their own ineptitude — and succeed in delighting us on every page.

Mort Walker again gives us a barrel of laughs in his marvelous cartoons concerning the most unprofessional soldier in the army!

### Beetle Bailey Books

# beetle bailey®
# NEW OUTFIT!

by
Mort
Walker

JOVE BOOKS, NEW YORK

BEETLE BAILEY: NEW OUTFIT!

A Jove Book / published by arrangement with
King Features Syndicate, Inc.

PRINTING HISTORY
Jove edition / May 1990

ISBN: 0-515-10313-6

Jove Books are published by The Berkley Publishing Group,
200 Madison Avenue, New York, New York 10016.
The name "JOVE" and the "J" logo
are trademarks belonging to Jove Publications, Inc.

PRINTED IN THE UNITED STATES OF AMERICA

10  9  8  7  6  5  4  3  2  1

EVERY DAY I THINK, "MAYBE **THIS** IS THE DAY I'LL HEAR FROM THE PENTAGON"

1-13

WELL, IT'S NOT TODAY, YOU JERK!

I HATE THESE NEW TALKING CARDS

MORT WALKER

YOU SHOULD TEACH THAT OLD BUZZARD A LESSON

WHY?

BECAUSE HE'S A LASCIVIOUS, WORLD-CLASS SEXIST!

WHAT CAN I DO ABOUT THAT?

GOOD MORNING, GENERAL

MORT WALKER

WHERE DO YOU THINK YOU'RE GOING?

TO SEE IF THERE'S ANYTHING GOOD TO SNACK ON IN THE KITCHEN

3-28

THERE WASN'T

MORT WALKER